May your heart
and your mornings
be joyful!

♡ Kayla

JOYFUL MORNINGS

mindful poems for inviting **happy** *days*

kayla floyd

art by emily walen

For Siri, Bjorn, Unni, and Ingrid -
You are my sweet love, bear, sunshine, and
wildflower. I couldn't imagine anything better.
For Tony - Word.

-ew

For information about special discounts for bulk pur-
chases, please contact Kayla@KaylaFloyd.com.

Illustrated by Emily Walen

Joyful Mornings/Kayla Floyd. —1st ed.
ISBN 978-1-7354870-3-8

For Brian and Chloe,
the sunshine in my joyful mornings.
Team Floyd forever.

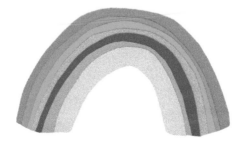

CONTENTS

Begin - 8

Begin

This book is both an offering and an invitation. It is a tiny portal for you to step into when you could use a reminder of the power of simplicity and the beauty of new beginnings.

I have never been a morning person in the traditional sense. I don't naturally rise early, and I adore lazing in my bed long after my eyes have opened and my body has stirred.

And yet, I am morning's biggest fan. I fill with wonder and gratitude at the thought of each new day, and I am humbled by the realization that we are granted a fresh possibility with every sunrise.

The poems in this book are laced with that wonder. They are tiny offerings of love and simplicity, and they are welcoming invitations of ease and flow.

Use this mindful guide however your heart desires. Perhaps you keep it on your bedside table and turn to its healing frequencies each morning. Maybe you carry it with you throughout your day, finding connection and presence no matter the hour.

However you choose to explore these pages, may the words and images inside help you unwind and exhale as you gently choose a new perspective.

May your mornings be joyful.

breathe

Morning's here; the day's begun.
Time to greet another sun.
Before you stir or blink your eyes,
Here's a practice you could try.

Take a pause and breathe in deep.
See how much air your lungs will keep.
Hold it there while you can.
Then let it out and take a scan.

Notice how your body feels.
Those sensations will reveal
If you need a few more breaths
To get into a state of 'yes.'

Your breath's a tool and a friend.
It carries love and nourishment.
It gives you strength and energy.
Try it out and you will see.

One mindful breath is all you need,
Or maybe two or twenty-three.
Take it slow; enjoy the feeling.
Steady breaths are extra healing.

Use your thoughts to guide its path.
Send the breath to what may ask
For extra space, extra love;
Give yourself an inner hug.

With your breath your body knows
It's time to wake, it's time to go,
It's safe to move, it's safe to be
Wondrous you and wondrous me.

thank

Now that you've filled your precious self
With sacred breath that fed your cells,
Let's invite another way
To help begin this happy day.

Your mind might want to moan and whine
And tell your body it's not time
To get this morning underway,
That bed is where you will stay.

Here is where you flex your might,
And tell yourself that it's alright.
Here is where you offer grace,
And say inside, *It's okay.*

Choose a thought that softens you,
And find a way to wiggle through
The crunchy feelings morning brings
When waking up sort of stings.

Thoughts like, *Thank you for this life.*
Thank you for this breath inside.
Thank you for the love I'm shown.
Thank you for the great unknown.

Being thankful is the key
To lifting thoughts easily.
It moves your mind from *Yuck!* to *Yes!*
And helps your body drop the stress.

Gratitude is morning's friend.
The birds sing it without end.
Sing your thanks from your heart,
And joyfully your day will start.

Smile

There you are, still in bed,
With a soul that's being fed
With sacred breath and loving thoughts.
Let's keep it going, could we not?

Let your cheeks slide up and out.
This isn't time for a pout.
Dreading the day won't make it quit,
So you might as well welcome it.

Invite a smile on your face.
Give it room, a little space.
See if all that love within
Can bloom into a happy grin.

Here's the thing about a smile.
It can travel many miles.
It can spread from you to me.
It can jump from face to knee.

That's correct, you heard it right!
Even knees can feel the light
Of one smile's happy glow.
You never know where it will go.

Give it a try if you dare...
Send your smile to your hair!
Now whoosh it around to your toes;
Then let it land on your nose.

Can you smile with your heart?
What a day you will start
When you let yourself play
With this trick everyday.

intend

Don't get up yet; don't you move.
There's another way to find your groove.
You've breathed and thanked, smiled too.
Now it's time for you to choose.

Before your feet touch the floor,
Before your body finds the door,
Ask yourself right where you lay,
How do I want to feel today?

What would you like your day to hold?
What wondrous things could unfold?
What way of being will you invite
To keep your heart open and light?

Perhaps you want to have more fun?
Or are there things to get done?
Would you like to be with friends?
Or do you need to go within?

Inviting intention into your mind
Gives you a compass to help you find
A guiding thought and feelings that
Tell you where your energy's at.

It's like a map, a special plan
To help you through the day at hand.
Knowing how you want to feel
Helps manage what the day reveals.

Intentions help you stay on course;
They lead you back to your source.
Search your heart right here and now;
Intend within and then allow.

enliven

It's time to move, it's time to rise.
Enliven your body, open your eyes.
Wiggle your toes, extend your arms.
Let your sighs be your alarm.

Remember your body is just a suit,
A place for your soul to spread its roots.
It's important to notice and care for it too,
And offer it time to gently renew.

Spread into your body like a glove.
Give it patience and lots of love.
Feel the air on your skin.
Notice the warmth from within.

Wrap your arms around yourself
And offer a hug to every cell.
This body is a sacred friend,
A safe place that you are in.

As you leave your comfy bed,
Move your neck, roll your head.
Twist your waist, circle your hips.
Bend your knees, open your lips.

Maybe you want to touch your toes
Before you reach for your clothes.
Balance on a single leg?
Do your thing, go ahead.

Keep it loose, connect with play
As you start this mindful day.
Stretch your muscles, move your bones.
This human house is your home.

Care

There are little things we all do
To start each day fresh and new.
Brushing teeth and wrangling hair,
What to eat and what to wear.

Living in this human form
Means these tasks are the norm.
It's how you choose to greet these chores
That will shape your joyful morn.

Can you act with love and care
And help yourself stay aware?
Can you find joy and ease
Moving like a gentle breeze?

Gaze into your own reflection.
Can you make a real connection?
Look into your precious eyes.
Can you say something kind?

You are fun, creative too.
I am glad that I am you.
You are special as you are,
Like a bright shining star.

Take a breath and soak it in.
There's always time to go within.
Tap your heart and feel your feet.
Let your breath and body meet.

Even on the busy days,
Taking care is the way
To find your rhythm and your peace
And welcome joy easily.

Savor

Morning's full of simple pleasure
Waiting there for us to treasure.
The magic of the rising sun,
The whispers of a day begun.

See how the light fades in slow,
How the sun begins to glow
A dazzling orange, a vibrant yellow,
The entire sky waving *Hello*!

Icy blues and bubble gum pink,
A swirl of color with every blink.
Lilac fades to gauzy white,
An endless stream of healing light.

Nature's way of starting new,
Another chance with every hue
To cling to hope, to opt for peace,
To find the joy that morning brings.

There's beauty in the quiet too.
Simple sounds meant for you
To savor with an open heart,
Let them wow you with their art.

A morning song from a bird,
The loving tone of a word
From the ones you hold dear,
Medicine you're meant to hear.

When you pause to drink it in,
You'll feel the wonder there within.
You'll sense the buzz that nature brings
To fuel your heart and spread your wings.

Connect

Hearts are bound by little strings,
Invisible cords where love zings
Back and forth between each other
Spreading goodness like a butter.

No matter where you are in space,
Connection always finds a way
To hold two hearts hand-in-hand,
Strongly bonded as a band.

Morning is a sacred time
To offer thanks for these lines
That bind you to the ones you love
And channel light from above.

Tap your heart and feel the tingle.
Notice where you sense the mingle
Of what is you and what is them,
What's going out and coming in.

Think of those you hold dear.
Some are far, and some are near.
Think of those who've passed on.
Love is never truly gone.

Light the flame inside your chest.
Be the joy you want expressed.
Send them peace and gratitude.
Allow the love they've sent to you.

Hold it there warm and tight,
A place you go to feel the light.
Face your day calm and ready
Knowing love flows in steady.

hug

Spread your arms super wide.
Push them out from side to side.
Now cross each one across your chest
Like a giant hugging vest.

Squeeze your hands against your skin.
Bend your elbows, drop your chin.
Close your eyes and feel the love
Wrapped up in one simple hug.

Hold yourself in sweet embrace.
Take your time; it's not a race.
Say inside, *I am here*
With myself who I hold dear.

Sense your spirit warm and true.
It's the pulse that flows through you.
Feel the body where it thrives.
Explore the corners where it hides.

Energy is a field
Where intent is revealed.
When you hold your sacred being,
Practice care, feel the meaning.

Offer grace and patience too.
Hug the worry out of you.
See if you can squeeze out fear.
How much space you can clear?

You are worthy of this love.
You are worthy of this hug.
Simple acts make giant waves,
And love grows with each embrace.

dance

Gentleness is morning's gift,
A little way to help us lift
Our sleeping heads and resting hearts
And find a soft and flowing start.

But once you've found your waking groove,
Your body just might want to move.
What better way to greet a day
Than finding music, pressing play.

Calm piano, gritty blues,
It doesn't matter what you choose.
Look within to how you feel,
And find a tune that appeals.

Allow the beat inside of you.
Move your body strong and true.
Let your arms sway with love.
Use those feet to cut a rug.

Feeling stuck? Dance it out.
Notice anger? Give a shout.
Use your body to transmute
What your mind can't compute.

Movement is an easy way
To shift your mood and convey
The feelings that don't make sense,
The thoughts inside that feel dense.

Shake it out and move your limbs.
Laugh or cry, tears or grins.
Dancing is your sacred art,
And now's the perfect time to start.

laugh

Lightness is an inner state
That paves the path to create
A day of joy, a life of fun,
An always-shining inner sun.

Ease and flow thrive in light.
Even fear can't hold tight
When you lighten from within
And change the state that you're in.

There's lots of ways you could try
To smooth the crunch you feel inside.
Dancing helps, hugs too,
Breathing deeply to renew.

But laughter holds its own power.
It's like a happy inner shower.
It tells your body and your brain
That joy and love are free to reign.

Try to make a little chuckle.
Practice ease; skip the struggle.
Think of something extra goofy,
Maybe from a funny movie.

Let the sound roll right through,
Thinking thoughts that tickle you.
Let your chest and belly shake,
And feel the joy in its wake.

Morning laughter offers hope
And tethers you like a rope
To vibrant hues instead of gray,
To better feelings through your day.

bask

There's power in a mindful pause,
Drawing breath just because,
Sitting still, slowing thoughts,
Finding peace that you've sought.

Beginnings mark a precious time
For rituals and love divine.
Moving through with peace and calm,
Mornings are a soothing balm.

Close your eyes and center in
On the buzz you feel within.
Let your mind soften too.
From your thoughts, come unglued.

Ask your body to relax,
Hips loose, jaw slack.
Pierce the river of your breath.
Watch it lift away your stress.

Notice in this quiet scene
How the space flows between,
Giving way to deep release,
Connecting you to inner peace.

Revel in the light inside
Giving thanks for this life.
Memorize this precious feeling.
Bask in all that it's revealing.

No matter what you face today,
Know that love finds a way.
No matter where you go from here,
Your joyful morning's always near.

ACKNOWLEDGMENTS

The birth of this sweet book would not have been possible without the love, support, and inspiration of the following people. I send my deepest thanks…

To Alexandra Franzen and Lindsey Smith for your endless support, incredible wisdom and epic pep talks.

To my writing partner Mayuri Amarnath for helping me stay tethered to my voice and encouraging me through the storms.

To my talented designer Emily Walen for your inspired artwork and loving dedication to bringing my vision for this joyful book to life.

To Dr. Joe Dispenza for first introducing me to the power of 'creating your day' all those years ago and for teaching me how to lift the veil.

To Thich Nhat Hanh for providing the inspiration for this truly tiny book and for reminding me of the inherent power in simplicity.

To Laraaji for your Sun Piano and Moon Piano albums. Your music transports me to sacred places deep within myself and was the faithful soundtrack for the creation of this book.

To my parents Leisa Moore and Kenny Burns, my bonus mom Jeane Burns, and my Mema Willa Smith for being amazing grandparents to Chloe and giving me the peace of mind to shift out of mom-mode into creative-mode.

To my big sister Lacy for sharing a safe and loving container for both our sorrows and our joys and for co-creating the frequency of hammam-level-good.

To my daughter Chloe for your encouragement and excitement about all my writing projects and for being the best friend a person could ask for.

To my husband Brian for your partnership, support, love, laughter and friendship and for always believing in me.

ABOUT THE AUTHOR

Kayla Floyd is a mother and avid meditator who is passionate about mindful living. She writes feel-good books that empower and inspire. Other works by Kayla include **Wondrous You: Empowering Poems for Magical Kids** and **Wondrous You: The Coloring Book**. Visit her online at www.kaylafloyd.com.

Printed in the USA
CPSIA information can be obtained
at www.ICGtesting.com
JSHW071321170823
46688JS00007B/202